C000227587

Gerry Thing

Stay cool & look mean.

Lubin Tales

Dedicated to Sarah and David Mitchell

Published by
Lubin Publishing
4 Stokecliffe House,
114 Park Road,
Bristol BS16 1DT
www.zerolubin.org

ISBN 978–0–9563077–0–5

Photographs and text by Gerry King

Designed and illustrated by Louise Burston

Printed by
HSW Print, Tonypandy, South Wales

Lubin Tales

GERRY KING

Photographs by Gerry King
Designed by Louise Burston

Published by Lubin Publishing
Printed in Wales

Contents

I want to make memories   12

Tough Love   16

You were weird at school   20

Poodle Faker   23

Performance   28

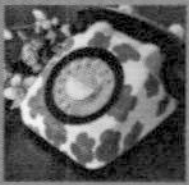

Flower Power   30

It's hard to be a good man   33

Take it easy... but take it   40

Boxing Clever 42

1947 V-12 Lincoln 45

Something for the weekend 49

Bachelor Bicyclette Brothers 55

Let me save you 58

Acknowledgements 61

About the Author 62

take it easy . . . but take it

STUDS TERKEL
1912–2008

Welcome to a world of small town debauchery and intercontinental dubious intent.

Lubin Tales is a collection of illustrated 'micro-fictions' – short stories and musings by artist and performer Gerry King, presented to you by his alter ego, Doctor Zero Lubin.

These tales benefit from being read aloud in a celebratory fashion, preferably to your loved one. However, much joy can be derived from the comfort of singular recitation.

I want to make memories with you

I considered myself the personification of 1950s utility furniture — wardrobes and chests of drawers made from wooden frames of decommissioned Mosquito dive-bombers.

I always wanted a china cabinet, a shiny, mirrored curio-cuddler from a retro shop in Camden Lock. Cosseting a sufficient elegance of whatnots, the evidence of my lonely travels.

Please let me make memories with you.

WINTER GARDENS PAVILION

ctor of Entertainments : I. DAVIES   Pavilion Manager : D. S. ASHMAN

WESTON-SUPER-MARE

Monday, 28th July, 1952 at 7.30 p.m. —

Weston-super-Mare Sportsmen's Organisation (B.B.B. of C.) present a

rand Professional Boxing Tournament

Terrific 6 3-min. rds. Middleweight Contest at 11-st 3-lbs.

N DESBOROUGH   v.   JOHNNY MUDGE

Hanwell.   **Torquay.**

d tough two-handed battler.   All-round fighter and great crowd pleaser

at Special Attraction - 8 3-min. rds. Welterweight Contest at 10-st. 8-lbs.

PAUL KING

QUAY. Unbeaten to date. Brilliant ex-amateur record. First time here.

al up-and-coming youngster and No. 1 contender for area title honours.

v.

MICK ANGELL

CKLEWOOD. Beaten Ken Tizor, Arthur Garratt, Johnny Godfrey, Ronnie
e, Fred Morris, Benny Leonard, Johnny Jackson, and on his last appearance
K.O.d. Joe Pring. Good all-action fighter. Don't miss this fistic treat.

Special 6 3-mins. rds. Featherweight Contest at 9-st. 5-lbs.

arry RAMSDEN v. Brian GOODWIN

F. Hereford. Unbeaten to date.   **Fulham.** Tough all-action Boy.
classy boxer.   Won 5. Lost 1.

Tough Love

As a boy I used to go with my dad to a pub in London, on the Old Kent Road, called the Thomas à Becket. Dad had once trained there. On the bar in a corner was a game I would play while my dad had a drink with his pals. I'd kneel on a bar stool, cheese and onion crisps and a bottle of cola at my elbow. This game involved holding a handle that had an insulated loop and guiding, with a steady hand, the loop over an undulating wire suspended between two posts. If you touched the wire with the loop a loud bell would go off.

In the early 1950s before I was born my dad was a professional boxer; one of his televised fights was from the Grand Pier Pavilion at Weston-super-Mare. He travelled there by train and stayed at the Grand Atlantic Hotel. He told me he did his roadwork – his running – along the seafront. The guy my dad fought was called Rees Moore and he was originally from Maerdy near the Rhondda Valley in South Wales.

In the early 1990s I stayed in Weston-super-Mare. It was a significant period of my life; a time when I had to put up a fight. Looking back, I've come out all right

– Weston gave me a neutral corner. I have always regarded the town with affection and gratitude and I was genuinely upset by the news of the pier fire.

In 2008, I went on a day-trip to Weston during the wettest August in a hundred years. Looking through a viewfinder capturing the twisted metal at the end of the pier, I thought of the Thomas à Becket bar game. It was overcast with showers yet there was a Churchillian spirit of 'fighting the weather on the beaches'. The holiday memories of my childhood – fish and chips, cups of tea in 'proper china mugs', buckets and spades – all the familiar accessories of the British seaside resort.

Maybe the decline of the cheap foreign holidays, coupled with the credit crunch, has contributed to the long line of coaches at their 5 p.m. pick-up points along the seafront. Or maybe there is a simpler explanation: people like coming here.

The workers aren't coming from the coalfields of South Wales or the car plants of Birmingham's Longbridge any more but the people reflecting the rich cultural mix of these locations are still faithfully visiting Weston. I ask if I can take a photo of the tangled pier from inside one of the coaches from Wales. The people are warm and friendly, asking me to come back with them. Outside, a huddle discuss cigarette etiquette with the driver of the coach; inside, the plastic bags of seaside booty, oversized beach balls and stuffed toys from the fairground. Memories that will be fixed by the pier fire and the wet summer of 2008.

You were weird at school and your house is filthy...

but you're still my friend

Simon went to Germany during a school holiday. He brought me back a piece of concrete from the Nuremberg stadium.

Frequently, after school, I would go to his house and watch *Magpie* on the television. His mother was incapacitated due to a debilitating illness, therefore high-level dusting was simply out of the question. His father was in gaol for swimming pool fraud.

I miss these gentle distractions.

Poodle Faker

Motoring slowly along a superstore B-road on the outskirts of a one-time cattle town called Newton Abbot, I see an elderly priest walking along the road. I'm not sure if he is a priest or a vicar. He looks stencilish, a man in black wearing gold-framed spectacles. He is carrying a black brass-clasped attaché case.

I'm on my way to see the Poodle Faker. Within half a mile I spot another holy man of the cloth, younger than the first, wearing a contemporary rucksack. It's a beautiful crisp February morning. The thought enters my mind he could be a 'media' priest, a regular on Radio 2 with Terry Wogan. I drive cautiously after this sighting, not sure if this situation, seeing two priests, falls into any category of superstition. I imagine the priest sharing with his 'tuned-in radio flock' something of his adventures:

'As I ambled through the village I was aware of numberplates passing me with the numeral 3 in them. Interestingly, there were more numberplates with 3, representing the Holy Trinity, than there were with 6, representing the enemy. This is good news.'

I create these distractions to comfort myself. I remember the actor Timothy Spall, in the Poliakoff film *Shooting the Past*, uttering the phrase 'but I know how life works'. Those words resonated with me because I don't – I just don't do life very well. I am drawn to individuals such as the Poodle Faker; I believe it is my duty to record their activity like a British Studs Terkel, to document their rich contribution to the esoteric, to a disappearing social history. No doubt within the clip-boarded parameters of Volkswagen Polo-driving support workers he could be pigeon-holed, given a mental health title in the curious critical language of the numbingly well-pensioned dull.

A Series 244 Volvo with faded burgundy paintwork is parked close to a potting shed. I pull into the narrow weed-tufted driveway and almost immediately Clive the Poodle Faker appears. He stands in the doorway with the hyper-intense air of a potential violent suicide; I could picture him falling backwards from the parapet of a French-engineered suspension bridge, arms outstretched like a John Lewis Jesus.

A tired grey Bovey Tracy bungalow shows blistering render and rusty drainpipes, the type of dwelling to draw the attention of unscrupulous doorstep merchants driving tired Transit vans, advertising on magnetic signs their Acme business pay-as-you-go number. The type of transient trader who when paid in cash smells the notes for clues of concealment. The bungalow suggests pelmets, small Wade figurines and the scratch marks of departed cats. It had indeed originally belonged to Clive's Auntie Pamela, a compulsive knitter, spinster and volunteer.

I have never known an easy Clive; every Clive I've met was trammelled and had bony hands. Particular names appear to attract certain qualities. I cite Vivienne and Wendy as strong examples. Clive reminded me of a boy I went to school with called Paul Pendle. Paul had been born old. I saw him many years later, when he was in his forties, wearing council uniform overalls and tending a bowling green in Paignton. It looked like he had arrived. It was perfect. I remember he dithered as a youth and now he emanated the air of a gracefully moving bowling-green expert – placing pellets, stepping softly.

As we go through to the lounge I notice Clive is shod with highly polished brown brogues, wearing well-pressed tweed trousers and a duck-egg blue sleeveless cardigan. Clive is in context but he does not dither. He points to the rotary dial telephone, saying: *'If my thoughts were hand cream I would ring more often.'* As I sit down in a green velvet 1950s Zanuso armchair I ask him what he meant by the comment. *'Oh, it's just a saying I collected from one of my Barbaras.'*

Clive always refers to his women friends as Barbaras. Apparently his latest Barbara possesses a remnant of Isadora Duncan's fateful scarf and drives an original red Fiat 500. He tells me he had met her at the autumn fair held in the local community centre. She had been selling copies of her self-published romantic novella entitled: *The Amorous Butcher's Love Slate* – a torrid tale of passion amongst sawdust, dead beasts and the cold metal of mincing machines.

Clive could be regarded as a man who spends too much time in the society of women, engaging in such activities as tea dances and séances – events that actually occur more often than one would think in this day and age.

Whilst it all sounds flippantly amusing, let us not lose sight of Clive the Poodle Faker poised on the parapet of the suspension bridge. Oh yes, there exists a very real feyness, a loneliness within this man and within this bungalow of someone else's life. I notice that when Clive speaks he moves one of his hands, fingers pointing vertically, in an up and down fluttering motion, like an absolution. I have seen this mannerism before; the American filmmaker David Lynch has the very same habit.

I ask Clive why he is attracted to older women. He tells me that he felt he'd always left things too late and being in the company of 'Barbaras' gives him the sense of a head start. I can't tell if he is serious or not. He flicks the tassels of a brilliantly coloured shade on a turned-wood stand and points to a Cadillac-fronted Bakelite radio and then elaborates:

'When I was a schoolboy I had a friend whose mother was the mistress of a successful bookmaker. I would often go round to their flat – it was above an antique shop. She had flame-red hair and smoked Embassy cigarettes that she theatrically lit with a heavy Dunhill lighter. I always thought she was like a lady in a glossy magazine. There was glamour about her, but I didn't know what it was: the lipstick-stained cigarette ends in the Johnny Walker ashtray, the perfume and the high heels. What clinched it for me was she listened to Radio Four. I'd never heard it before. She wore small pearl earrings and poodle brooches with diamanté eyes. I can never remember eating anything when I visited. We listened to plays on the radio, where I heard things like: "Fix yourself a drink while I get ready." There was always a promise of something – suitcases with travel tags, French windows, car doors slamming, tinkling glasses and RP endearments. This woman opened possibilities that I could not name at the time but they stayed with me. She was that older woman and for me she was never a mother.'

Performance

On Monday 26th March 1956, Paul King was conveyed by Jack Turner in a black Austin Seven to the Great Yarmouth Hippodrome. Jack was a one-eyed dangerous driver and Paul King's manager. In 1928 Jack had fought the formidable Sunderland-based Cast Iron Casey, winning on points. Incidentally, Turner was the name of the character Mick Jagger played in the 1969 cult film *Performance*.

Paul was to win this bout, and later meet fairground attraction Flexible Phyllis for a hot bath and a quiet night at a local hotel.

GREAT YARMOUTH HIPPODROME

A CLIFF BUTLER PROMOTION

BOXING

MONDAY, 26th MARCH

Doors open 7 p.m.   Commence 7.45

Important Eight (3-min.) Rounds Welterweight Contest at 10 st. 9 lb.

PAUL

KING

...rquay. Will be remembered for his sensational win over Boswell St. Louis. King is now rated fifth best welterweight in Great Britain. **v.**

LEO.

MALONEY

...ingdon. Having defeated Johnny Fish here Leo must be considered a great test for King.

Six (3-min.) Rounds Lightweight Contest at 9 st. 11 lb.

CLIVE

...AMPLING
...rwich **v** SAMMY

...ODELL

Nigeria

...ix (2-min.) Rounds Middleweight Contest at 11 st. 8 lb.

...RED JACKSON
Cambridge **v**

...ETER KEYWIN

Chelsea

Six (3-min.) Rounds Lightweight Contest at 9 st. 13 lb.

MAURICE MURFITT
Cambridge **v**

GEORGE SPENCE

Leeds

Six (3-min.) Rounds Lightweight Contest at 9 st. 12 lb.

MARTIN TOLAN
Leeds **v**

TERRY RUSSELL

Poplar

Flower Power

The giving of flowers gladdened my heart. The way you received the bouquet and cradled it like a small child.

Somewhere love had become orphaned, somewhere I had become lost.

I watched a trinity of films: *The Lives of Others*, *Little Miss Sunshine* and *The Night Porter*. I then contemplated the nature of love, made several telephone calls and decided to make a grand gesture with a spray of silk flowers purchased from Mr Alignment.

It's hard to be a good man and a good thief too

The Stealerant

He found the button on the top of the handbrake ratchet rather sexy tonight, the precise clicking of the ratchet appealing to his institutional sense of order – a sense of order encouraged in a mid-seventies children's home. He parked a ten-year-old gunmetal-grey Jaguar neatly between the lines away from the well-lit ticket machine. After locking the car, this unrepentant charity-shop stealerant takes a short moonlit walk to the high street. The examination of donated bags is performed in the deep-recessed doorways; this deed is one of several in his creative repertoire. His actions are driven by a complex fusion of necessity, superstition and a genuine inquisitiveness. These particular actions could be construed as theft but this is not our concern – we are merely observers.

Two days earlier on a coastal path in Devon: 'Gimme the matches', she said. 'Oh, I love the smell of matches. I remember this old fella who used to go into the newsagent, he wouldn't buy anything unless it was

British. You know the matches, with the Union Jack. He used to buy Parade as well, top-shelf stuff like these.' The thin big-haired kohl-eyed girl took the matches from the stealerant and struck a flame under the dog-eared porno mags placed in the middle of a flint stone circle. After a little flappy breeze blow, the paper ignited and bare girls' grinning started burning.

Back on the street tonight he wanted books and small figurines for his own self-fulfilling intimacy. Some objects he would sell at locations where cash was paid and no questions asked, others he'd cherish and contemplate. He had cultivated a network of elderly antique dealers with whom transactions could be concluded over tea and cake and in the summer months fruit squash and lollies. These characters, exclusively ladies, were the aunties he never had, each possessing an equal measure of avarice and calculated eccentricity. The stealerant believed most sincerely in the existence of psychometry, a phenomenon whereby one individual can absorb the energy of another through physical contact with their possessions. He thought that in this world you needed the bones of a saint to get by.

As the embers scattered skyward, she said: 'I think it's really creepy. Why are there always magazines like this in the woods?' Without an answer, she continued, 'When are you going to get some more nice pieces and when are you moving in with me?' He knew something was expected so he said: 'Just chill, it's going to be fine'. As a distraction, he neatly folded a red handkerchief with white spots and appreciated the tactile texture of the natural fabric. They both walked away from the fire holding hands.

Not all the items he obtained were through dishonest acts. Seeking the possession of purity through ecclesiastical association he once bought a small pine bookcase from a convent jumble sale, hoping it would retain some spiritual benevolence that would permeate his life. His feelings changed when he read of allegations against priests. He could only hope that a tainted priest, with a sweep of a cassock, had not brushed too closely near the bookcase when visiting the convent.

He had filled the bookcase with a selection of his prized Olympia Press first editions, trawled from notably affluent areas. Initially he wasn't aware of the collectability of these green Parisian paperbacks. It was one of his lady dealers who, as a young woman, had lived at the Beat Hotel in Paris in the late 1950s.

She actually knew some of the authors and pointed out the value of the books after seeing one peeping out of his jacket. Whilst not worth a fortune, the titles *Naked Lunch* and *Story of O* commanded pleasant returns amongst collectors.

However, when dough was tight these books would eventually be sold, along with the bookcase, and the compulsion of obtaining an object with 'good energy' would be played out again. For comfort, when he was extremely stressed, he would talk to Baby La Strange, his secret friend and creative muse of at least two disturbing decades. She had been there for him when charity shops still sold electrical goods, when it was possible to buy a decent dolls' house with a brass hinged roof and latticed windows. She would always whisper what he needed to hear in order to justify whatever act of gentle banditry he was committing.

It was Baby La Strange's voice, the melodic melding of Zaza from *Hector's House* and the ghost of Eartha Kitt that led him to the green biodegradable sack that had been placed tight to the deep-recessed doorway of the shop. Opening the sack revealed a faded BOAC complimentary flight bag, zipped and angular, bulging with the promise of treasure.

Crouched and rummaging, the stealerant sensed the presence of somebody behind him. Turning, he saw an elderly man and caught a whiff of 4711 Eau de Cologne. The man, overcoated and trilbied, just stood watching, his bulky frame backlit from the street. Mr 4711 put his big stitched leather gloves together as if he were praying and said: 'During the war my Uncle George was torpedoed twice. The first time he was washed up on the coast of Spain. Then later as part of the Atlantic convoys, he was picked up by a U-boat. The captain of the U-boat asked him what cargo his ship had been carrying. Uncle George replied "Nuts". The German captain slapped his face. Some years later when Uncle George was liberated from a prisoner of war camp he took, as the spoils of war, a silver cigarette box from a bomb damaged German home.'

Mr 4711 gestured to the stealerant to get up. It was almost an act of absolution. The stealerant left the bag and followed Mr 4711 to the shop entrance where they both watched as a whistling cyclist with a flashing light on his head raced down the pavement opposite and a model train hooted and circled in a bright-red fronted toyshop window. He continued, 'Uncle George always had BSA motor bikes, he would take my Aunty Beatrice to Brighton in the bomb-shaped sidecar. Even though she polished the silver cigarette box she never liked it. They died, two years apart, within sight of that cigarette box, both of heart attacks.'

The hands of Mr 4711 had something of Jack Palance about them as he handed the stealerant a small wrapped object and strolled away. A black cab passed, its bright interior light illuminating the fixed face of a raven-haired woman; a clattering shutter was pulled down on a discount booze store with the façade of a 1960s police station.

The stealerant walked swiftly back to the Jaguar, feeling resplendent in his pirate trousers. Quite out of the blue, he found himself ruminating on the phrase: *'Politics is show business for ugly people.'* He realised there is so much ugliness in the world but there is also oodles of beauty: his kohl-eyed girlfriend with the fire in her eyes.

The ratchet was silent on the way down. The stealerant steered the motor out on to the main road.

Take it easy... but take it

'If there had been no Elvis there would be no Beatles' (John Lennon).

'Without Studs Terkel there would be no Zero Lubin' (Gerry King).

Studs Terkel was a good friend of Nelson Algren who wrote the book *The Man with the Golden Arm*. The film was set in Chicago and Frank Sinatra played the part of Frankie Machine.

Studs Terkel celebrated ordinary lives through his writing and had a daily radio show on WFMT Chicago. Studs Terkel is a spectacular name. President Barack Obama, a fellow Chicagoan called Studs *'a national treasure'*.

Boxing Clever

Nobbins: colloquialism for money thrown into a boxing ring by the crowd in appreciation of a good contest.

Paul King commenced his pugilistic career on an Anderton & Rowland fair ground. He assiduously saved his 'nobbins' until he had the required amount to purchase a royal blue and cream holiday caravan near Sidmouth.

BOXING

WATFORD TOWN HALL
At 8 p.m. ★

PROMOTER:
Mr A. E. MALLETT. B.B.B.C.

**FRIDAY,
SEPT. 10th**

★ At 8 p.m. ★

TELEVISION NIGHT

TWO IMPORTANT WELTERWEIGHT CONTESTS
TO BE TELEVISED AT 9.20 p.m.

EACH EIGHT (3 min) ROUNDS

JACKIE
BRADDOCK

MANCHESTER. Central Area Welterweight Champion. v.

PAUL
KING

TORQUAY. Beaten Peter Smith. Leo Maloney. Rees Moore. etc.

ALF
DANAHAR

WANDSWORTH. Southern Area Welterweight Champion. v.

JOHNNY
FISH

HARLOW. Strong challenger for Area Championship

SPECIAL SIX (3-min.) ROUNDS RETURN LIGHTHEAVYWEIGHT CONTEST

ND CAIN v. DON STOCKER
WATFORD   TORQUAY

★ Also **THREE STRONG SUPPORTING CONTESTS** ★

UCED PRICES (inc. Tax) 3/-, 5/-, 7/6, 12/6, 17/6 and 22/6

LICENSED BAR APPLIED FOR

1947 V-12 Lincoln

France, late February 2008, I discover an old car with a Parisian numberplate abandoned in a small wood near Grenoble. The distance between Paris and Grenoble is 298 miles or 479 kilometres. A local farmer named Coco furnishes me with these details: his father had bought the car from a Monsieur Albertini, who owned the garage in Grenoble where the car had been towed. The engine had seized because no one had checked the oil. The car is a 1947 V-12 Lincoln Sedan with suicide doors – rear doors that open towards the front of the car. The term 'suicide door' originates from the 1930s and denotes a combination of terrible chassis flex and unreliable single acting catches. This caused the doors to open over bumps or whilst cornering and without seatbelts it was very easy to fall out. Originally the shell of the Lincoln was sky blue and the interior was beige. The steering wheel, door lock stalks and window winder handles were claret-coloured Bakelite.

Coco's father realised it was cheaper for him to purchase the Lincoln and remove the chassis to make a tractor-trailer, rather than buy a factory-made trailer. Even though it was twelve years after the war there was still a shortage of basic materials. The clock was removed from the dashboard and found its way to Coco's cousin Muumuu's kitchen. It wasn't wired up but looked good on the windowsill especially when the sun caught the chrome.

Monsieur Luc, the proprietor of a rock'n'roll themed coffee bar, bought the leather seats. Parts of the car were to find themselves scattered over several farmhouses and village businesses. Luc also found a notebook pushed down the back of the front bench seat. I was lucky enough to see this notebook; inscribed inside the front cover in italic flourish were the words:

'Be not inhospitable to strangers lest they be angels in disguise'.

CHABLAIS
Arve
GENEVOIS
Annecy
Arly
BAUGES
Bourg
St. Maurice
Isère
Chambéry
Moutiers
GRANDE
CHARTREUSE
Arc
Grenoble
Isère
Romanche
VERCORS
Briançon
PELVOUX
Pô
Drac
Drôme
DÉVOLUY
Mont
Dauphin
Durance
DIOIS
Buech
Tallard
Ubaye
Sisteron
VENTOUX
Digne
Puget Théniers
Castellane
Verdon
Durance
Var
Nice
Arc
Argens

Something for the Weekend

Due to diabolical rent increases during the late 1980s, Paul the Continental Hairdresser relocated to new premises overlooking a bowling green. A remaining constant within the shop was the two La Reine Restocrat chairs, blood red and cream. They embodied 1950s Cadillac cool.

On the pine-panelled wall by the atomic coat-stand, Italianate males modelled 1960s hairstyles. A finishing touch favoured by the older customers was the Boston Square Back.

Bobby Secateur, bulky, sharp-suited, baby-faced, fine childlike dark hair, was the director of a wholesale refrigeration outlet and a regular of Continental Paul's. He would regale him with tales of gambling, womanising and drinking with a rich raft of characters. Paul would invariably explete at the end of these numerous salacious episodes that Bobby delivered with relish. Bobby had one particular story that, on each occasion, they would bizarrely treat as if it was the first time it had been told.

Paul's

	from
GENTS' HAIRCUTTING	£6.00
BOYS' HAIRCUTTING	£5.80
WET SHAMPOO	£8.50
DRY SHAMPOO	
SHAMPOO & STYLING	£9.00
FRICTION	
SHAVING	
LONG HAIRCUTTING	
SHAMPOO & SET - LONG HAIR	
CUT, SHAMPOO & SET	£12.50
FLAT TOP STYLING	£13.50

The tale involved a chronically alcoholic pub landlord called Roy – a Londoner, slight build, grey hair thinning, whose wife had left him, taking their boys with her. Roy's bar faced the sheer side wall of an Odeon cinema and was entered from some steps between two main roads. It was long, dark and narrow, a Courage cock emblem standing proud from a nicotine-stained hardboard pelmet. The brewery only delivered barrelage to this bar for cash. A daily ritual involved Roy opening early and selling enough pints to enable him to go to the off-licence for a bottle of scotch.

This was a long way from when Roy, a rock'n'roll aficionado, drove an Impala Bel Air Biscayne Del Ray bought from an American airbase in the late 1960s. Upstairs Roy had nearly a dozen pairs of narrow bottomed jeans purchased from Paul the Boxer in a moment of nostalgic madness. He couldn't sell them, wouldn't wear them and now didn't care.

Bobby entertained Paul the Continental Hairdresser with a version of events that occurred within the bar that would be funny if it wasn't so steeped in the malady of alcoholic tragedy. One particular rainy November morning Bobby had popped in for a swift half. On the jukebox Johnny Cash was singing 'I walk the line' loudly into the emptiness. Bobby had known the beer would be flat but felt a loyalty to Roy for past good times.

Roy leant on the bar drinking scotch and tea from a chipped blue and white Cornishware mug, the only light in the pub coming from the jukebox. They discussed the latest Courage promotion that involved collecting small numbers and putting them on a card. The prize for completion of the card was £1000. The number everybody was after was 873. They talked near misses and lucky touches, and then Roy drew Bobby's attention to a guy at the jukebox. This is the part of the story Paul the Continental Hairdresser loves; he always tilts his grey haired Elvistic head and smiles with a wide-eyed wonder as Bobby builds the tale.

Bobby looked over toward the jukebox – there was no one there. Roy didn't like his attitude – the jukebox guy – in fact he'd had trouble with him before and this is the final straw, he's going to bar him. At that moment Bobby placed a hand on Roy's arm and suggested he didn't do that as the jukebox guy had been buying him drinks all morning.

Roy poured some scotch into his mug, drank, blinked and straightened a Colt 45 beer towel with both boney shaky hands. Paul the Continental Hairdresser would, as if on cue, brush the back of Bobby's neck and repeat *'buying him drinks all morning'*.

The Bachelor Bicyclette Brothers

The premises were originally purchased by Bernard Sartain, the racy Parisian Bichon Frisé breeder. It was a period of magnificence with cabaret and orchestras regularly appearing in the marquee erected outside each summer solstice. Valmera & Clemson Hume, the exhibition dancers, provided an attractive feature with some danses d'élégance. Guests who were to grace the building included the fearless British explorer, Sir Farley Juju-Soames and Trigger Mostel, the infamous Hollywood film star.

The history of the location is extremely interesting as the contents of cabin trunks in the attic attested. However there was an issue of 'ungracious atmosphere' that was not conducive to the peace of mind of the current residents, the Bachelor Bicyclette Brothers.

Deviant vibrations were detected in the bedroom and partially in the hallway. Through an ingenious use of angled mirrors, muscle-builder Brian, a vacationing feng shui practitioner, was able to deflect these abnormalities away from the building in the general direction of the annual Dauphiné Libéré.

The Bicyclettes had always had something of the Francophile about them and they transferred effortlessly.

Let me save you from yourself

She was svelte, sexy, sensation-seeking and Scorpio – worked as a nurse and liked to get her fingers into the ward trolley for the dolly mixtures. He was a border-line-functioning chemically dependent criminal creative with interests in Brixton and Totnes. In ecstasy 'loved-up mode' they would swan about Brighton and Hove in a midnight-blue Sunbeam Rapier playing Barry White on the eight track.

Envy is a strong word – let me now save you from yourself.

Acknowledgements

Many thanks to all those who have contributed to the realisation of *Lubin Tales*, with a special mention to Louise Burston, Matt Seaman, Glenn Carmichael and Patrick Cooke at the Bakelite Museum, Somerset.

Also, not forgetting all the friends and family who have supported me over the years . . . *you know who you are.*

About the Author

Gerry King is a writer, photographer and performer. Born in London, his first ever foray into writing and publishing was a three-page carbon copy magazine made when he was in care during the early 1970s. Until the early 1990s Gerry carried out extensive research in subjective malfeasance, experiencing a wide range of colourful environments and characters from secure government institutions to seaside winter lets, city squats and international hotels. His work history covered most aspects of low-status survival and decidedly dubious self-employment. He comes from the old school of battered Transit vans and fading walnut dashed predatory Jaguars with big boots.